Colin McNaughton's
ABC
and
THINGS

· Ernest Benn ·

A
is for All at sea

B
is for Bending the rules

C
is for Crime wave

D
is for Dead end

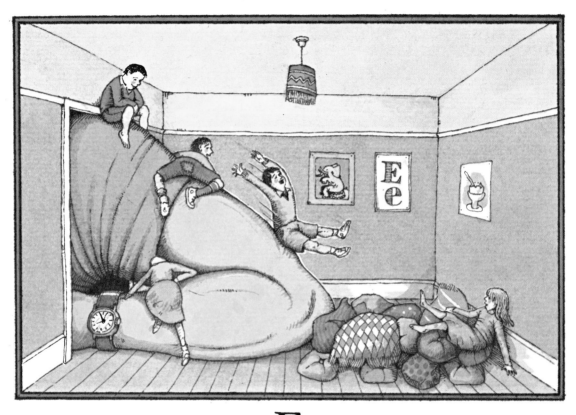

E
is for Elbow room

F
is for Flying off the handle

G
is for Gate~crashing

H
is for Hay fever

I
is for In the soup

J
is for Jumping the queue

K

is for Keeping mum

L
is for Letting off steam

M

is for Moving house

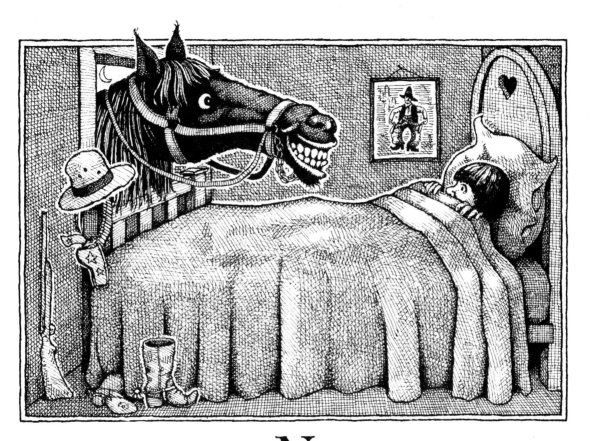

N
is for Nightmare

O

is for Over the moon

P
is for Potatoes in their jackets

Q

is for Quiet as a mouse

R
is for Running a temperature

S

is for Storm in a teacup

T
is for Too big for his boots

U

is for Under the weather

V
is for Visiting card

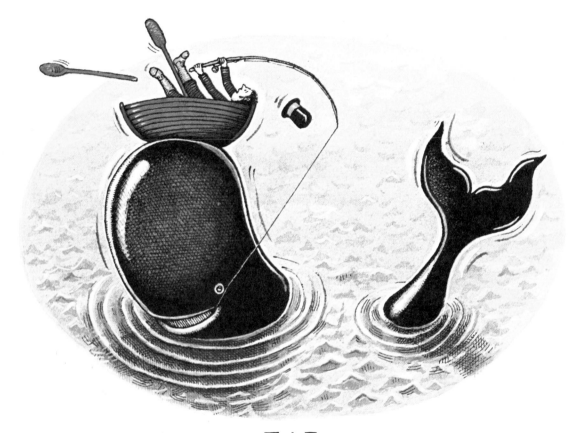

W

is for a Whale of a time

X

is for X marks the spot

Y
is for Yawning gap

Z
is for Zipping along

First published 1976 by Ernest Benn Limited
25 New Street Square London EC4A 3JA
& Sovereign Way, Tonbridge, Kent TN9 1RW
© Colin McNaughton 1976
Printed in Great Britain by W. S. Cowell Ltd, Ipswich

ISBN 0 510-02004-6